PRIVATE VIEWS

Private Views

★

NEW POCKET CARTOONS

by

OSBERT LANCASTER

GRYPHON BOOKS LTD, LONDON

Earlier volumes of Pocket Cartoons still available:

LADY LITTLEHAMPTON AND FRIENDS

STUDIES FROM THE LIFE

TABLEAUX VIVANTS

Other works by Osbert Lancaster:

PROGRESS AT PELVIS BAY

PILLAR TO POST

HOMES SWEET HOMES

CLASSICAL LANDSCAPE WITH FIGURES

THE SARACEN'S HEAD

DRAYNEFLETE REVEALED

FAÇADES AND FACES

First Edition 1956

Printed and bound in Great Britain by Jarrold & Sons Ltd, Norwich, for Gryphon Books Ltd, 37/39 Essex Street, London

FOREWORD

It is gratifying to be able to report that, despite depth-psychology, sulphonamide and Miss Nancy Mitford, behaviour-patterns of the time-wasting classes have not been noticeably modified during the past year. And it is not generally expected that the adoption of the five-day week will materially affect those of them who are enrolled in the Civil Service. Everyone, in fact, continues to grow more and more like themselves as the years roll by. Or so at least it seems to the heavy lidded eyes of middle age; which may well be a source of distress to scientific humanists, but hardly to cartoonists. And so with the customary acknowledgements to the Editor of the *Daily Express*, I once more beg to draw the attention of the long-suffering public to the appearance of another volume of exhaustive researches proving absolutely nothing, except, perhaps, the universal application of the Doctrine of the Fall.

O. L.

"Feelthy Flags?"

"You know, darling, I'm just a teeny bit worried about Jennifer these days—she seems to get so easily overtired."

"Believe it or not, young lady, but your dear mother here helped me to break training the year I stroked Leander in the Grand!"

8

DEO. GRATIA
REG. MAG. BRITT
IND. IMP. DEF. FID

THE TIMES

PRINCESS
MARGARET

Daily Mirror

TOWNSEND
LATEST

Daily Mail

INTERVIEW
WITH
"CRAWFIE"
Exclusive

BISHOP
SAYS

9

"A fat lot of use three-lane carriageways are going
to be for two-lane cars.

"Willy, darling, if I understood Mr. Butler correctly, from now on we must try very hard to owe the tradesmen more and the bank less."

"Now dear, perhaps you see why mother has always warned you never to accept presents from strange dress-designers!"

"Well, darling, she may be Bermuda-rigged, but as far as I can see, she is still wearing that old blue pullover and those rather badly cut slacks."

"The Way to the Downs? Well, you goes straight on past the Ministry of Agriculture's research station, turn left by the beech wood wot the Forestry Commission cut down, on past the Prison Without Bars, right by the airfield, and you'll come to a notice saying 'War Department—No Admittance!' That's it!"

"If the march of science continues at its present rate, by 1965 it'll take twelve hours to reach the moon and a fortnight to get to Hyde Park Corner!"

"Guess what—I'm the County Planning Officer, and I've just issued a demolition order under the Act!"

"Darling, do you remember the dear, distant days
when we used to make jokes about the French
railways?"

"Damme, sir! It's not that I've got anything against the wops personally—it's just that one doesn't expect to meet them down a gentleman's mine!"

"Philip darling, you know I love you, but I'm
terribly short of oxygen!"

"Vite, vite, Thérèse, c'est le yacht des Dockers! !"

'Darling Mummy,
    Do you remember your saying that the only way
really to learn French is to live in a family . . . ?'

"Look, Maudie! The poor fella's broken his cast!!"

"And when did your Grace first become convinced
that you had incurred the hatred of your peasants?"

"But, Excellency, I've been madly pro-Enosis ever since he gave that *lovely* party on his yacht at Monte Carlo! !"

"Ladies, Ladies! Please remember that you're prima donnas and stop behaving like air-marshals!"

"Thank you, I know all about the importance of mother love, but if you don't stop pinching my nylons you're going to feel more emotionally insecure and unwanted than you've ever felt in your life! ! !"

'Je suis Princess Fuerstenberg
Tu es Princess Fuerstenberg
Elle est Princess Fuerstenberg
Nous sommes Princess Fuerstenberg
Vous êtes Princess Fuerstenberg
Elles sont Princess Fuerstenberg

"Darling, do let's just wait for the bit when they tell us which one isn't using you know what!"

"Really, darling, you must try to remember that a witch-hunt is only a witch-hunt until it's supported by the Astors—then it becomes a crusade."

"He says he retains the pleasantest memories of your glorious country and vividly recalls the happy days he passed in the Crimea!"

"Unofficial strike 1954, unofficial strike 1955, and a special good conduct medal for five year's continuous service without once stopping at a request stop."

"Darling, why is it called the *Secret* Service?"

"He says he's always had a profound admiration
for the Soviet way of life!"

"One of these days it's going to occur to some intellectual giant in London Transport to embark on the revolutionary policy of collecting fares as well as raising them!"

"All right, granted you're my true love, do you
mind telling me what I'm expected to do with it?"

"Peace, and good will toward Lady Mount-
pleasant! Peace and good will toward Aunt Ella and
all at the Pines! Peace and good will toward
Archdeacon and Mrs. Fontwater! Peace and
good will. . . ."

"Well if that's No. 11 then Pam's right, there is going to be a rift in the Cabinet!"

"Darling, he's got everything—but everything—
and it's all tax-free as he's with UNO!"

"—no sooner had Ali Baba pronounced the magic words 'open sesame' than he found himself in an enormous cave packed with Cadillacs, Coca-Cola, and the largest block of oil shares east of Suez!"

"—and when you've quite finished singing songs of Araby it might interest you to learn that this is the Israeli Legation!"

"By Jove, Mr. President, I bet Sir John Rothenstein envies you—not having any pictures that even the Irish are likely to pinch!"

"Now's yer chance, comrades! Follow the party line and win a lovely bowl o' goldfish!!"

"Of course it was all a terrible mistake, but you
know how these things will happen!"

"Oh, to hell with Nancy Mitford! What I always
say is—if it's ME it's U!"

"It's all very well the P.M. saying we'll stand by our friends in the Middle East, but what on earth makes him think we've still got any friends in the Middle East?"

"The Dowager Countess of Littlehampton wants to know why she's not being shadowed—she says she's just as anti-Communist as Malcolm Muggeridge and twice as dangerous!"

53

"Bicentenary or no bicentenary, Ma says she's had Mozart and do you want her to come out and tell you what you can do with your magic flute?"

"Well, dears, and how much farther have we all
gone up the spiral since I saw you last?"

"Before we go any further, Mr. Leadenhall, will you please understand that I don't mind the gentle pressure of the knee, but I WON'T have the Bank rate explained to me!"

"The problem as I see it is how to convince the Russians that there's no defence against the H Bomb without letting the public get hold of any damfool idea about cutting down on generals!"

"Gertrude, you have misled me! That is not the splendid little creature who used to sing that charming ditty about the Isle of Man at the old Tivoli!"

"Mr. Van Hamburger, will you please realise, once
and for all, that there are certain British assets
which will for ever remain beyond the reach of
dollar-imperialism!!"

"According to Freud, deep down inside me there's
a father-image with an expense account."

"But grandpapa, you don't mean to say you ever actually walked around dressed up like that?"

"Faites vos jeux, messieurs et mesdames, faites vos
jeux! Rien ne va plus!!"

"I wonder if Colonel Nasser has ever seen a nationalised canal?"